Black Hat Bob

Story written by Gill Munton
Illustrated by Tim Archbold

Speed Sounds

Consonants   *Ask children to say the sounds.*

f ff	l ll	m	n	r	s	v	z s	sh	th	ng nk

b	c k ck	d	g	h	j	p	qu	t	w wh	x	y	ch

Each box contains one sound but sometimes more than one grapheme.
*Focus graphemes for this story are **circled**.*

4

Vowels

Ask children to say the sounds in and out of order.

a	e	i	o	u
at	hen	in	on	up

ay	ee	igh	ow	oo
day	see	high	blow	zoo

Story Green Words

Ask children to read the words first in Fred Talk and then say the word.

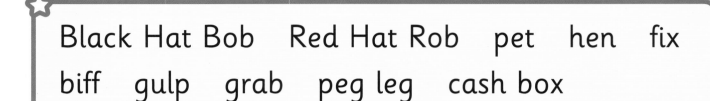

Black Hat Bob   Red Hat Rob   pet   hen   fix

biff   gulp   grab   peg leg   cash box

Red Words

Ask children to practise reading the words across the rows, down the columns and in and out of order clearly and quickly.

he	said	no
my	I	you
be	of	your
the	put	said

Black Hat Bob

Black Hat Bob
is on his ship.

This is his peg leg.

This is his pet hen.

This is his cash box.

This is Red Hat Rob.

"I will grab that cash box," he said.

"Get off my ship!" said Black Hat Bob.

"No," said Red Hat Rob.

"I will not."

"I will fix him,"
said Black Hat Bob.

Biff biff

Gulp!

Questions to talk about

Ask children to TTYP for each question using 'Fastest finger' (FF) or 'Have a think' (HaT).

p.8 (HaT) What is a peg leg?

p.9 (HaT) Why do you think his cash box is so important?

p.10 (HaT) Why do you think Red Hat Rob wanted to grab the cash box?

p.11 (FF) What did Black Hat Bob say?

p.12 (HaT) Why does it say 'Biff biff'?

p.13 (HaT) Do you think Black Hat Bob will ever get the cash box back?